Writing *Stop The World* with Evie and Anthony Newley

Leslie Bricusse, Shirley Bassey and Anthony Newley

Leslie and Evie at the Oscars

Anthony Newley, Henry Mancini, Sammy Davis Jr. and Leslie Bricusse

Leslie Bricusse and John Williams

TOMMY TUNE

DR. DOLITTLE

EVERYBODY'S MUSICAL

Book, Music and Lyrics by Leslie Bricusse
Based upon The Doctor Dolittle Stories by H...
and The Twentieth Century Fox...
Book Revisions by Lee Tann...
www.drdolittlethemusica...

The Kennedy Center and Music Theater International
present the Original Cast Recording of

Roald Dahl's
Willy Wonka

FEATURING THE SONGS
"The Candy Man"
AND
"Pure Imagination"

MUSIC AND LYRICS BY
LESLIE BRICUSSE &
ANTHONY NEWLEY

ADAPTED FOR THE STAGE BY
LESLIE BRICUSSE &
TIM MCDONALD

DIRECTED BY GRAHAM WHITEHEAD

Leslie Bricusse and John Barry

Graham Mulvein with D & J Arlon
in association with Stage and Screen Music
and The Alexandra Theatre, Birmingham present
THE BRISTOL OLD VIC PRODUCTION OF

ROBERT POWELL in ROY BARRACLOUGH

LESLIE BRICUSSE'S

SHERLOCK HOLMES

THE MUSICAL

Book, Music and Lyrics by
LESLIE BRICUSSE
Based on characters created by
Sir Arthur Conan Doyle
Also starring
LOUISE ENGLISH
Cast Recording on TER CDs & Cassettes

11 MARCH – 10 APRIL 1993
BRISTOL BOX OFFICE: 0272 250250

Organ
Solo
Series

WHO CAN I TURN TO (When Nobody Needs Me) / All Organs #S3016

from the David Merrick - Bernard Delfont production
"THE ROAR OF THE GREASEPAINT
—The Smell Of The Crowd"

WHO CAN I TURN TO?

(When Nobody Needs Me)

Words and Music by
LESLIE BRICUSSE and ANTHONY NEWLEY
Arranged for All Organs by RUDOLF SCHRAMM

The Complete Work

Jekyll & Hyde

the gothic musical thriller

Music by Frank Wildhorn   Lyrics by Leslie Bricusse

NOAH'S ARK

THE INTERNATIONAL AWARD-WINNING SPECTACULAR

ANTHONY NEWLEY

in

Scrooge

THE MUSICAL

Book, Music & Lyrics by
LESLIE BRICUSSE

Based upon the CCF/CBS
Theatrical Motion Picture "SCROOGE"

LONDON'S CHRISTMAS CRACKER!

IT'S A MUSICAL WORLD
THE MUSIC AND LYRICS OF
LESLIE BRICUSSE & ANTHONY NEWLEY

Anthony Newley and Leslie Bricusse

PURE IMAGINATION

THE SONGS OF LESLIE BRICUSSE

HOT • GOLDFINGER • WHAT KIND OF FOOL AM I? • TALK TO THE WORLD • IF I RULED THE WORLD • GONNA BUILD A MOUNTAIN • THE ANIMALS • LE JAZZ HOT • FEELING GOOD

Leslie with Henry Mancini, Julie Andrews & Blake Edwards

Original artwork by AKA Productions

© 2015 by Faber Music Ltd
First published by Faber Music Ltd in 2015
Bloomsbury House
74-77 Great Russell Street
London WC1B 3DA

Printed in England by Caligraving Ltd

ISBN: 0-571-53925-4
EAN: 978-0-571-53925-3

To buy Faber Music publications or to find out about the full range of titles
available, please contact your local music retailer or Faber Music sales enquiries:

Faber Music Limited,
Burnt Mill,
Elizabeth Way,
Harlow
CM20 2HX

Tel: +44 (0)1279 82 89 82
Fax: +44 (0)1279 82 89 83

On Songwriting   04
About The Author   06

Can You Read My Mind   107
The Candy Man   100
The Dream   80
Feeling Good   38
Goldfinger   46
The Greatest   68
If I Ruled The World   27
Le Jazz Hot   111
Life!   84
London Is London   116
Mister Kiss Kiss Bang Bang   50
Music   136
My Kind Of Girl   12
My Old Man's A Dustman   08
A New Kind Of Music   140
On A Wonderful Day Like Today   33
The Only Man For Me   162
Paris In The Spring   131
The Perfect Song   166
The Pink Panther   21
Pure Imagination   97
Somewhere In My Memory   123
Talk To The Animals   60
Tell Me Who I Am   90
Thank You Very Much   75
Think Positive   158
This Is The Moment   127
Tomorrow With Me   155
What About Me?   150
What Kind Of Fool Am I?   18
When I Look In Your Eyes   57
Who Can I Turn To?   42
The World That I See   146
You Are All The Music   171
You Only Live Twice   53

On Songwriting

From those early childhood days when the dazzling dexterity of George and Ira Gershwin's talents first caught my ear and my attention, I have always been in love with the idea of songwriting – the marriage of words and music – in the same way that other people become obsessed with solving crossword puzzles. There are certain basic similarities of discipline between the two pursuits, and indeed making up crossword puzzles, as opposed to solving them, was one of my many early stepping stones along the path leading into the beautiful but sometimes impenetrable songwriting forest.

As with crossword puzzles, there is only one correct answer to the selection of every word of a lyric – the elusive *mot juste* – that one and only word in the entire language that expresses exactly, not approximately, whatever it is that you and the lyric are trying to convey. And it is not merely what the word means – it is also what it sounds like.

Likewise with the marriage of lyric to melody, the melody must not only entirely belong to, but also express and sound like, the lyric. The music illuminates the meaning of the lyric, just as the lyric can have only that melody and no other. They are the two reflecting halves of the same thing, and like the fine finished product of any art or craft, the two pieces must be seamlessly joined.

In parallel fashion, the very best film composers somehow always manage to complement and elevate the essence of a great movie with the beauty and sensitivity of their mood-capturing underscoring.

Writing a song takes as long as it takes. Sometimes minutes, sometimes days – even weeks. Extreme example: three-time Oscar winner Alan Jay Lerner once spent more than eight months writing ninety- one drafts of the eight-line lyric of the song 'On a Clear Day You Can See Forever', and threw ninety of the ninety-one away! At the opposite end of the spectrum, four-time Oscar winner Sammy Cahn always maintained, 'If a lyric can't be written in forty-five minutes, it can't be written!'

The great Oscar Hammerstein II laboured mightily for many weeks over the lyric of 'Oh, What a Beautiful Morning!', the opening song of *Oklahoma!* Finally he proudly presented it to his equally great composer partner Richard Rodgers, who put it on the piano, took one look and played it! Dorothy Hammerstein, Oscar's wife, at a luncheon honouring Jerome Kern's 'Old Man River', pointed out that it was in fact Oscar Hammerstein's 'Old Man River' and Jerome Kern's 'Da-da-di-di'! I myself once wrote eighteen songs for one key emotional moment in the musical movie of *Goodbye, Mr Chips*, and finally got it right on the nineteenth try (a) because the film had by now started shooting, and (b) because MGM was threatening to bring in another composer!

Like all living creatures, no two songs are the same, except a few by someone whose identity I am not prepared to reveal.

It would sound complacent and glib to brag that I wrote this melody or that lyric in under forty-five minutes. Equally, I would sound pretty moronic if I confessed it took me ninety-one drafts and eight months to write an eight-line lyric!

But, as we now know from the above evidence, either statement is capable of being true. The one wouldn't make me a genius any more than the other would make me an idiot. It's the nature of the beast. Songs have a mind of their own, and they and they alone decide and will tell you when they're ready to reveal themselves. And at the end of the day we admire Alan Jay Lerner and Sammy Cahn for the brilliant songs they both wrote – not for how long it took them!

Songs are like women or cats – fascinating, elusive, seductive, irresistible, infuriating, moody, demanding and contradictory creatures. The writer pursues them like some phantom fantasy – fascinated, intrigued and desperate to find out what they're really like. They should be approached with caution and respect – especially at night. The more promising and beautiful they appear, the harder they may be to catch. But not always. Sometimes they simply throw themselves at your head, and there's your forty-five minutes . . . Other times you have to woo and cajole them to make an appearance and show themselves. And there you have your ninety-one drafts and your eight months . . .

It's all part of the songwriter's never ending quest – the eternal search for beauty, romance and occasional perfection.

with Rex Harrison

Leslie at Cambridge University

About The Author

Double Oscar and Grammy winner Leslie Bricusse is a writer–composer–lyricist who has contributed to many musical films and plays during his career. He was born in London, and educated at University College School and Gonville and Caius College, Cambridge. At Cambridge, he was President of the Footlights Revue Club and founded the Musical Comedy Club. There, he co-authored, directed and performed in his first two musical shows, *Out of the Blue* and *Lady at the Wheel*, both of which made their way to London's West End. He also found time in the gaps to acquire a Master of Arts degree.

The late, great Beatrice Lillie plucked him out of the Footlights Revue at the Phoenix Theatre, and made him her leading man in *An Evening with Beatrice Lillie* at the Globe Theatre, where he spent the first year of his professional life writing another musical, *The Boy on the Corner*, and the screenplay and score of his first motion picture, *Charley Moon*, which won him his first Ivor Novello Award. That year he decided to drop the possibilities of directing and performing, and concentrate his career on becoming a full-time writer–composer–lyricist.

His subsequent stage musicals include *Stop the World – I Want To Get Off*, *The Roar of the Greasepaint – The Smell of the Crowd*, *Pickwick*, *Harvey*, *The Good Old Bad Old Days*, *Goodbye, Mr Chips*, *Henry's Wives*, *Scrooge*, *Sherlock Holmes*, *Jekyll & Hyde*, *Noah's Ark*, *Sammy*, *Cyrano de Bergerac*, *Kennedy*, *Sunday Dallas*, *Victor/Victoria* and *It's a Dog's Life!* He has written songs and/or screenplays for such films as *Doctor Dolittle*, *Scrooge*, *Willy Wonka and the Chocolate Fac- tory*, *Goodbye, Mr Chips*, *Superman*, *fi Hats for Lisa*, *Victor/Victoria*, *Santa Claus – The Movie*, *Home Alone I* and *II*, *Hook*, *Tom and Jerry – The Movie*, *Goldfinger*, *You Only Live Twice*, *The Last Emperor*, various Pink Panthers, *The Great Music Chase*, *Two for the Road*, *The Sand Pebbles*, *Sunday Lovers*, *Babes in Toyland*, *The Land Before Time*, *Bachelor of Hearts* and *The Pied Piper of Hamelin*.

Bricusse has written more than forty musical shows and films, and over the years has had the good fortune to enjoy fruitful collaborations with a wonderful array of musical talents, including Anthony Newley, Henry Mancini, John Williams, John Barry, Jerry Goldsmith, Jule Styne, Quincy Jones, Andre Previn, Frank Wildhorn and Pyotr Ilyich Tchaikovsky (whose *Nutcracker Suite* he adapted into a song score).

Bricusse is one of very few people in the world of stage and screen musicals who contribute all three creative elements – book, music and lyrics – to a show or film, a feat he has achieved some twenty-five times. He has also written words and music (but not the book) or book and lyrics (but not the music) to a further dozen projects in his various collaborations.

His better-known songs include 'What Kind of Fool Am I?', 'Once in a Lifetime', 'Gonna Build a Mountain', 'Who Can I Turn To?', 'The Joker', 'If I Ruled the World', 'My Kind of Girl', 'Talk to the Animals', 'You and I', 'Feeling Good', 'My Old Man's a Dustman', 'When I Look in Your Eyes', 'Goldfinger', 'Can You Read My Mind?' (the love theme from *Superman*), 'You Only Live Twice', 'Le Jazz Hot', 'On a Wonderful Day Like Today', 'Two for the Road', 'The Candy Man', 'This Is the Moment', 'Thank You Very Much', 'Crazy World', 'Pure Imagination' and 'Oompa-Loompa-Doompa-Dee-Doo'.

He has been nominated for ten Oscars, nine Grammys and four Tonys, and has won two Oscars, a Grammy and eight Ivor Novello Awards, the premier British Music Award.

Hundreds of Bricusse's songs have been recorded by major artists, including Frank Sinatra, Nat King Cole, Judy Garland, Aretha Franklin, Barbra Streisand, Sammy Davis Jr (who recorded sixty Bricusse songs), Tony Bennett, Shirley Bassey, Tom Jones, Petula Clark, Julie Andrews, Liza Minnelli, Andy Williams, Bobby Darin, Rex Harrison, Kate Smith, Elaine Paige, Anthony Newley, Michael Feinstein, Bette Midler, The Moody Blues, Nancy Sinatra, Lena Horne, Sergio Mendes, Nina Simone, Dionne Warwick, Robert Goulet, Matt Monro, Ray Charles, Ethel Merman, Placido Domingo, Jennifer Holliday, Danny Kaye, George Burns, Robbie Williams, Mariah Carey, Linda Eder, Diana Krall, Maroon 5, Michael Bublé, The Black-Eyed Peas, Muse, and Jennifer Hudson.

In 1989 he received the Kennedy Award for consistent excellence in British songwriting, bestowed by the British Academy of Song- writers, Composers and Authors, and was inducted into the American Songwriters' Hall of Fame – only the fourth Englishman to be so honoured – after Noël Coward, John Lennon and Paul McCartney.

Jekyll & Hyde, written with Frank Wildhorn, ran for four years at the Plymouth Theatre in New York, and has had many international productions around the world, the most recent in Brazil, Spain, Germany, the UK, Russia, Australia, as well as Japan, South Korea and other Far East territories.

The stage version of *Victor/Victoria*, written with Blake Edwards and Henry Mancini, which successively starred Julie Andrews, Liza Minnelli and Raquel Welch at the Marquis Theatre on Broadway, has since been seen worldwide in many international productions.

Bricusse's stage musical version of Roald Dahl's *Willy Wonka* opened at the Kennedy Centre for the Performing Arts in Washington DC in November 2004, after a prestigious world premiere in the East Room of the White House attended by President George W. Bush, Laura Bush and an invited audience. The show has since enjoyed thousands of productions across the United States.

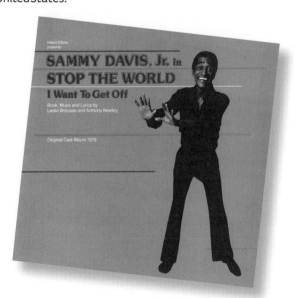

Another Bricusse perennial, his musical version of *Scrooge*, in which Anthony Newley starred at the Dominion Theatre in London's West End, is also seen each year in many productions around the world. The title role has been played by Richard Chamberlain in the US, Keith Michell in Australia, Ichimura in Tokyo, and currently stars Tommy Steele in his tenth season in the role in the United Kingdom, including two at the London Palladium in 2005–6 and 2012–13. A new Japanese production opened in Tokyo in 2013–14. An animated film version is currently in production in the UK, starring John Cleese as Scrooge.

For *Doctor Dolittle*, which played for four years in the UK, starring Phillip Schofield and almost one hundred animatronic animals created by Jim Henson's Creature Shop, Bricusse served as librettist, composer, lyricist and co-producer. A major US production followed in 2003, eventually starring Tommy Tune as Dolittle in 2006.

Cyrano de Bergerac, Bricusse's second collaboration with Frank Wildhorn, opened triumphantly in Tokyo 2009, and again in 2012–13. Further productions are scheduled to open in Germany and South Korea in 2015–16.

Sammy, Bricusse's biographical musical about his friend Sammy Davis Jr, broke every box office record when it opened at San Diego's Old Globe Theatre in 2009, and is now preparing both a West End production and a major motion picture.

The Great Music Chase, Bricusse's *Nutcracker* collaboration with Tchaikovsky, with screenplay and lyrics by Bricusse, is currently in production as an animated motion picture in the US and Canada.

Other current projects include *Pure Imagination*, Bricusse's song-book show containing sixty songs from sixty years of stage and screen songwriting, as well as the most ambitious project of his career, now completed, a lyrical adaptation of the instrumental works of George Gershwin (*Rhapsody in Blue*, *An American in Paris*, *Cuban Overture* and Concerto in F) entitled *A Few Words with George*. Bricusse plans to combine a world premiere concert in Sydney with an all-star recording of the work.

My Old Man's A Dustman

Words by Leslie Bricusse and Peter Buchanan
Music by Lonnie Donegan

Freely

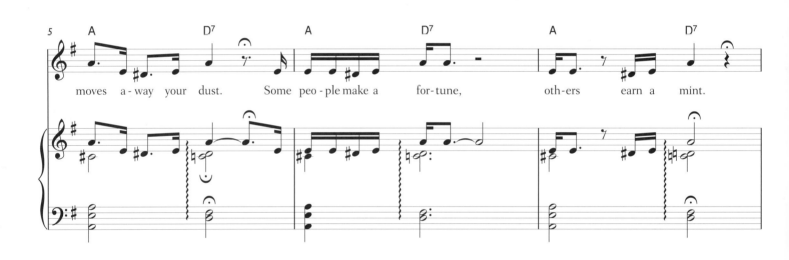

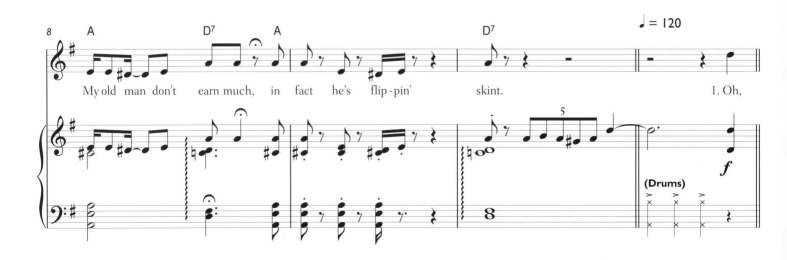

12 G .... D

(1.) my old man's a dust-man, 'e wears a dust-man's hat. 'E wears gore-blim-ey trous-ers an'
(2.) my old man's a dust-man, an' soc-cer is his sin. When Ar-se-nal are at 'ome, 'e's
(3.) my old man's a dust-man, 'e's got an 'eart of gold! 'E learned to dance the can-can tho'
(4.) my old man's a dust-man, 'e likes 'is drop o' beer! In fact, 'e glugs it down un-til it's
(Verses 5-7 see block lyrics)
(8.) my old man's a dust-man, an' take my word it's true. 'E's got a string o' swear words that would

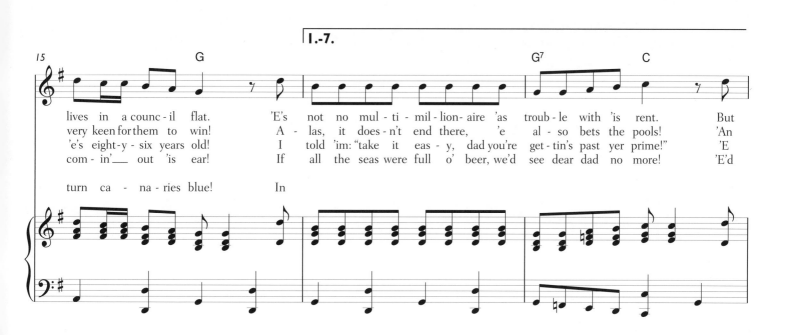

I.-7.

15 G .... G⁷ C

lives in a counc-il flat. 'E's not no mul-ti-mil-lion-aire 'as trou-ble with 'is rent. But
very keen for them to win! A-las, it does-n't end there, 'e al-so bets the pools! 'An
'e's eight-y-six years old! I told 'im: "take it eas-y, dad you're get-tin's past yer prime!" 'E
com-in' out 'is ear! If all the seas were full o' beer, we'd see dear dad no more! 'E'd

turn ca-na-ries blue! In

18 D .... G

on the 'ole a coun-cil flat is bet-ter than a tent! 2. Oh,
that is why 'is eight-een kids don't go to fan-cy schools! 3. Oh,
said: "well, when you're my age, son, it 'elps to pass the time!" 4. Oh,
chuck 'im-self off South-end pier and swim a-way from shore! 5. Oh,

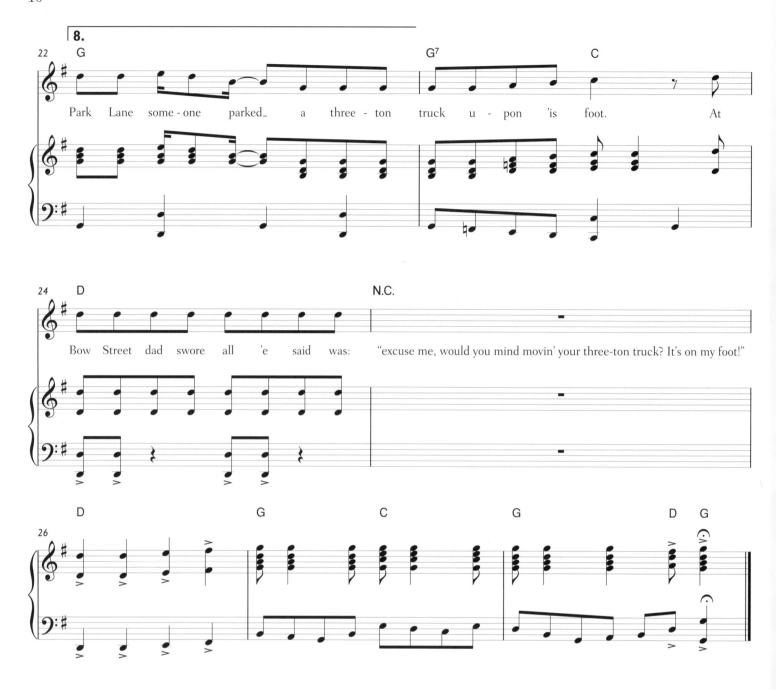

5. Oh, my old man's a dustman
'Is boots are size fourteen!
They're far too big for 'im
To try an' keep the buggers clean!

But yet I know 'e'll wear 'em
Till the day 'e kicks the box!
'E must die wiv 'is boots on
'E's got 'oles in all 'is socks!

6. Oh, my old man's a dustman
'E's slightly off 'is head!
'E never buys a calendar
In case 'e drops down dead!

It isn't that 'e's mean -
But 'e thinks wastefulness a crime!
That's why 'e buys 'is calendars
Just one month at a time!

7. Oh, my old man's a dustman
'E fought in World War One!
'E might've won a medal,
But 'e lost 'is flippin' gun!

'E stole some army dumplings
In a bloody great big pot
'E fed 'em to the Germans
An 'e killed the bloody lot!

MY KIND OF GIRL

Words and Music by LESLIE BRICUSSE

Recorded
by

**FRANK
SINATRA**

with

COUNT BASIE

on

REPRISE Records

ESSEX MUSIC

2/6

LIMITED

My Kind Of Girl

Words and Music by Leslie Bricusse

Sean Kenny's original design for "STOP THE WORLD"

SUMMER AT THE
STATE THEATER

A DECCA BROADWAY ORIGINAL CAST ALBUM

DAVID MERRICK
in association with
BERNARD DELFONT
presents

DECCA
BROADWAY

ANTHONY NEWLEY
in
STOP THE WORLD-
I WANT TO GET OFF
with
ANNA QUAYLE

A New-Style Musical

Book, Music and Lyrics by
LESLIE   ANTHONY
BRICUSSE   and   NEWLEY

Setting and Lighting by SEAN KENNY
Musical Supervision by IAN FRASER
Musical Director MILTON ROSENSTOCK

Orchestrations by
IAN
FRASER with DAVID   BURT   GORDON
              LINDUP   RHODES   LANGFORD

John Broome's Choreography Restaged by VIRGINIA MASON

Directed by ANTHONY NEWLEY

STOP THE WORLD
I WANT TO GET OFF

What Kind Of Fool Am I?

(from the Musical Production 'Stop The World - I Want To Get Off')

Words and Music by Leslie Bricusse and Anthony Newley

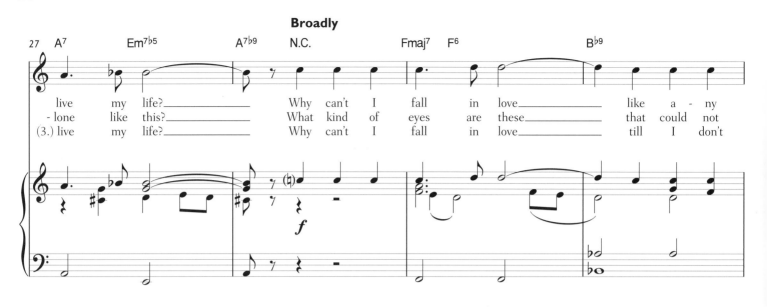

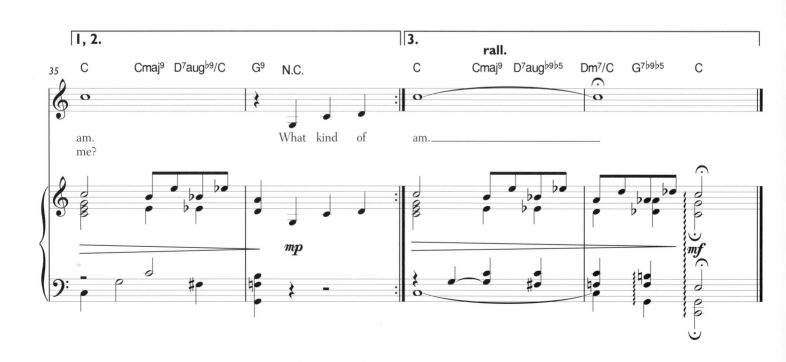

The Pink Panther

Words by Leslie Bricusse
Music by Henry Mancini

He'll have the clues tied up in the bund-le be - fore Jaques Clou-seau gets his brain in - volved.

Sud-den - ly my-ste - ry solved. Clou -

- seau! _____

(Scatting)

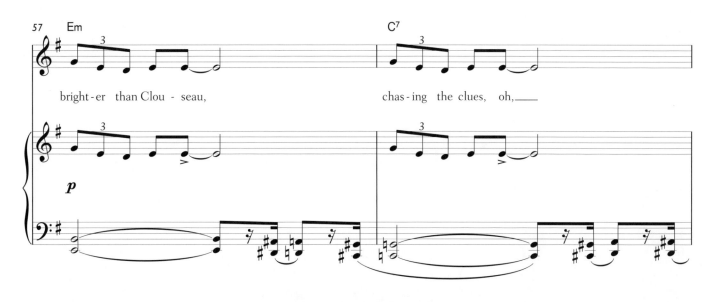

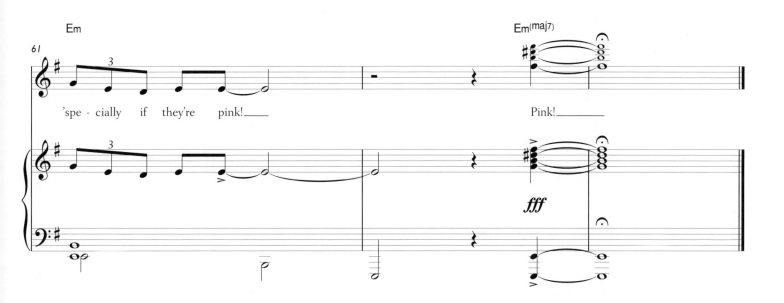

PIANO • VOCAL SELECTION

PICKWICK

THE MUSICAL

Based on Dickens' 'Posthumous Papers of The Pickwick Club'
Book by Wolf Mankowitz Lyrics by Leslie Bricusse Music by Cyril Ornadel

If I Ruled The World

(from 'Pickwick')

Words by Leslie Bricusse
Music by Leslie Bricusse and Cyril Ornadel

Steady moderate tempo

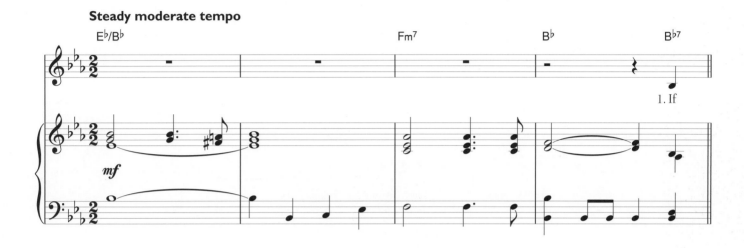

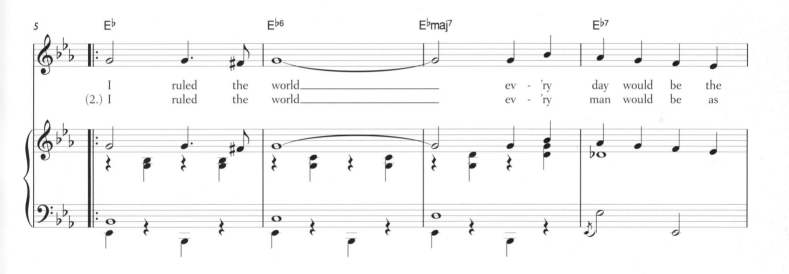

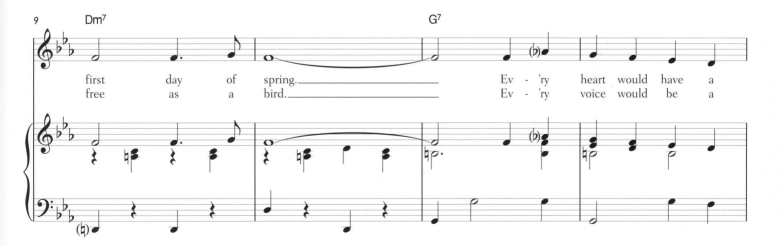

THE ROAR OF THE GREASEPAINT, THE SMELL OF THE CROWD
Book, lyrics & music by Leslie Bricusse & Anthony Newley; directed by Anthony Newley;
choreographed by Gillian Lynne; scenic design by Sean Kenny;
actors: Cyril Ritchard & Anthony Newley; detail of drawing, *NYT*, 1965

On a Wonderful Day Like Today

(from 'The Roar Of The Greasepaint - The Smell Of The Crowd')

Words and Music by Leslie Bricusse and Anthony Newley

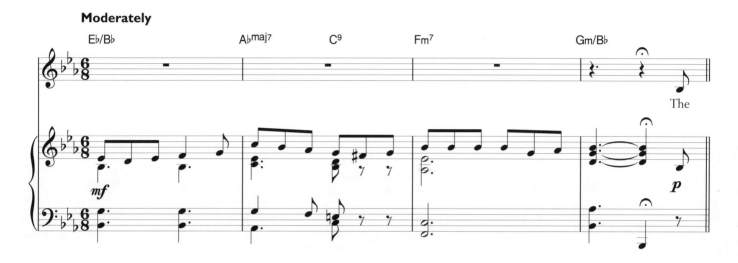

Feeling Good

(from 'The Roar Of The Greasepaint - The Smell Of The Crowd')

Words and Music by Leslie Bricusse and Anthony Newley

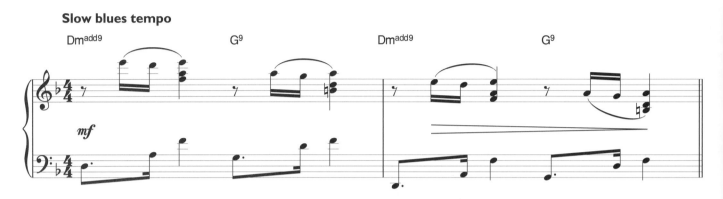

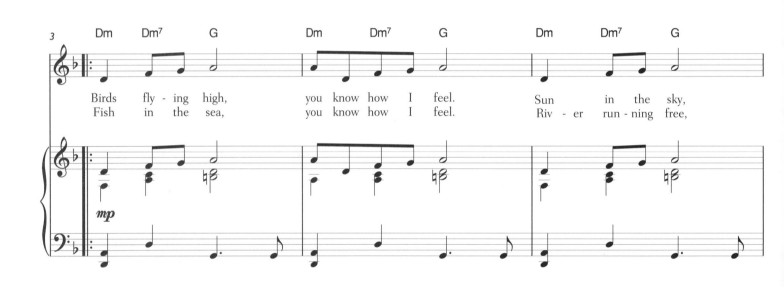

Birds fly-ing high, you know how I feel. Sun in the sky,
Fish in the sea, you know how I feel. Riv-er run-ning free,

you know how I feel. Breeze drift-ing by, you know how I feel.
you know how I feel. Blos-som on the tree, you know how I feel. It's a

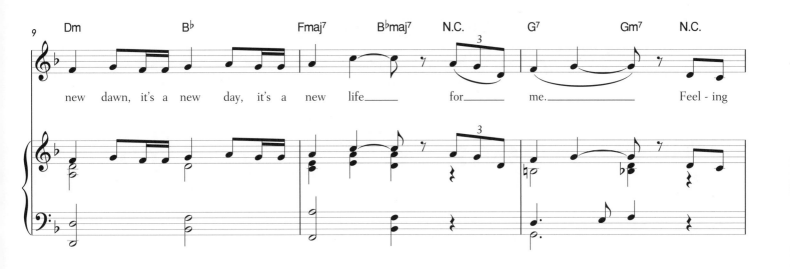

new dawn, it's a new day, it's a new life_____ for_____ me._____ Feel-ing

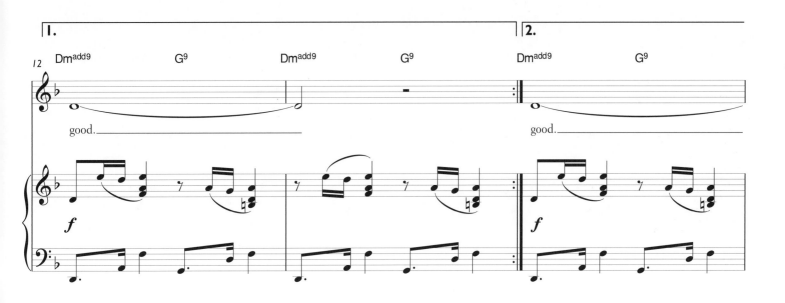

good._____ good._____

_ Drag-on-fly out in the sun, you know what I mean.

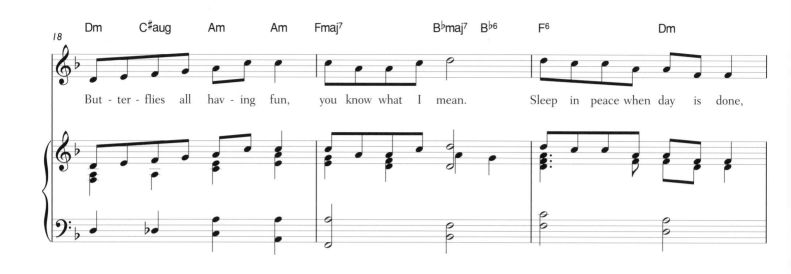

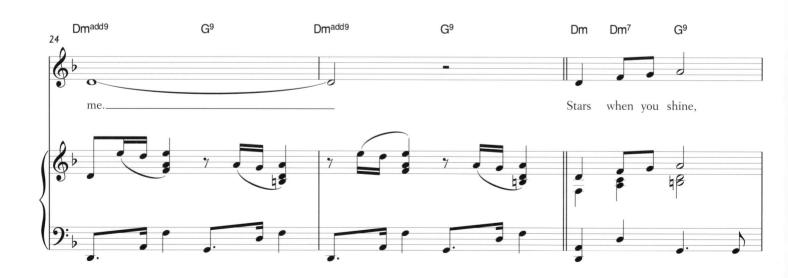

Who Can I Turn To?
(When Nobody Needs Me)

(from 'The Roar Of The Greasepaint - The Smell Of The Crowd')

Words and Music by Leslie Bricusse and Anthony Newley

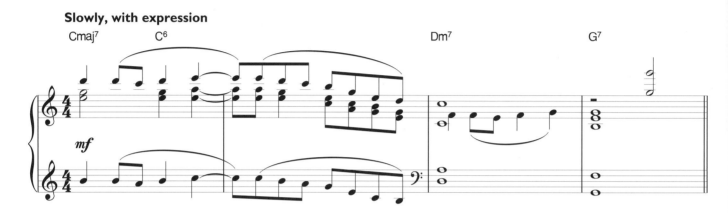

Who can I turn to_____ when no-bo-dy needs me?_____ My

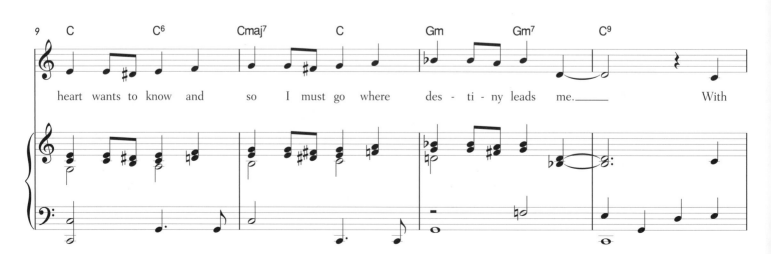

heart wants to know and so I must go where des-ti-ny leads me._____ With

© 1964 Concord Music Ltd
All Rights Reserved.

44

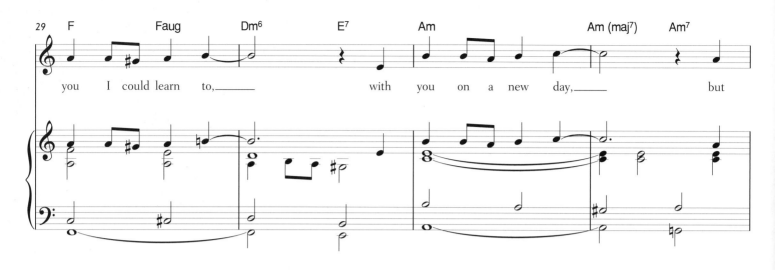

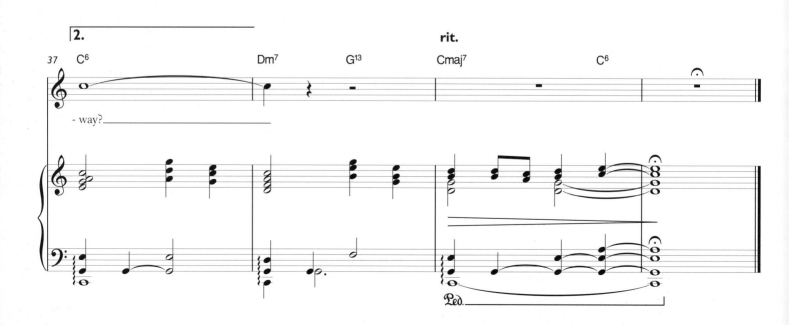

"You Only Live Twice"

MUSIC BY JOHN BARRY

LYRIC BY LESLIE BRICUSSE

SEAN CONNERY IS JAMES BOND

IN IAN FLEMING'S "YOU ONLY L
...and "TWICE" is the only w

Presented by
ALBERT R. BROCCOLI and HARRY SALTZMAN · LEWIS
Directed by

Produced by
ALBERT R. BROCCOLI and HARRY SALTZMAN · JOHN BARRY · Produc

PANAVISION* TECHNICOLOR ORIGINAL MOTION PICTURE SOU
AVAILABLE ON UNITED ARTISTS

UNART MUSIC CORPORATION

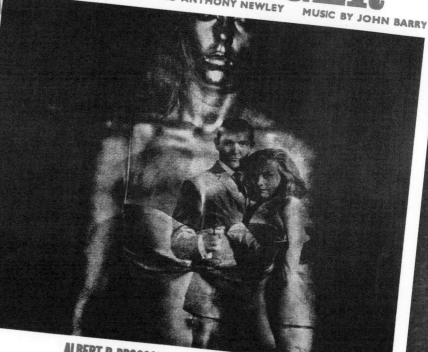

GOLDFINGER

LYRIC BY LESLIE BRICUSSE AND ANTHONY NEWLEY   MUSIC BY JOHN BARRY

ALBERT R. BROCCOLI & HARRY SALTZMAN PRESENT

SEAN CONNERY AS JAMES BOND 007
IN IAN FLEMING'S GOLDFINGER
STARRING HONOR BLACKMAN AS PUSSY GALORE TECHNICOLOR
GERT FROBE AS GOLDFINGER
SHIRLEY EATON · TANIA MALLET · HAROLD SAKATA & BERNARD LEE AS 'M'   SCREEN PLAY BY RICHARD MAIBAUM & PAUL DEHN
PRODUCED BY HARRY SALTZMAN & ALBERT R. BROCCOLI   DIRECTED BY GUY HAMILTON   EON PRODUC
UNITED ARTISTS MUSIC LTD.,
Mortimer House, 37-41 Mortimer Street, London W.1.   Express

Prints

Goldfinger

(from 'Goldfinger')

Words by Leslie Bricusse and Anthony Newley
Music by John Barry

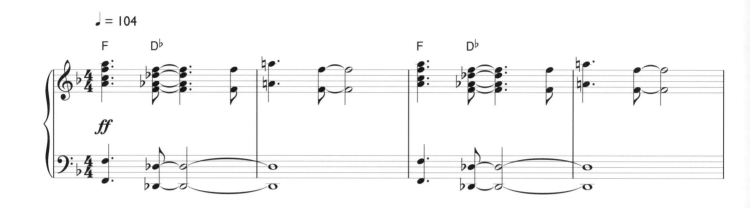

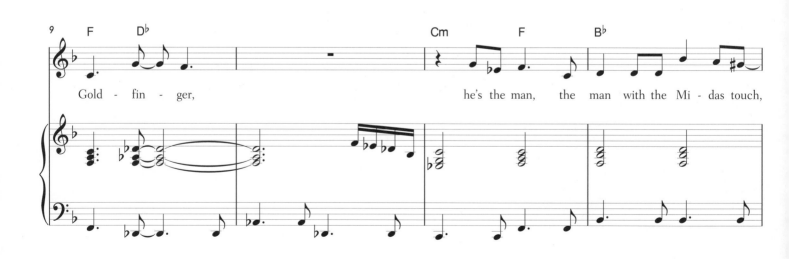

Gold - fin - ger,   he's the man,   the man with the Mi - das touch,

Mister Kiss Kiss Bang Bang

(from 'Thunderball')

Words by Leslie Bricusse
Music by John Barry

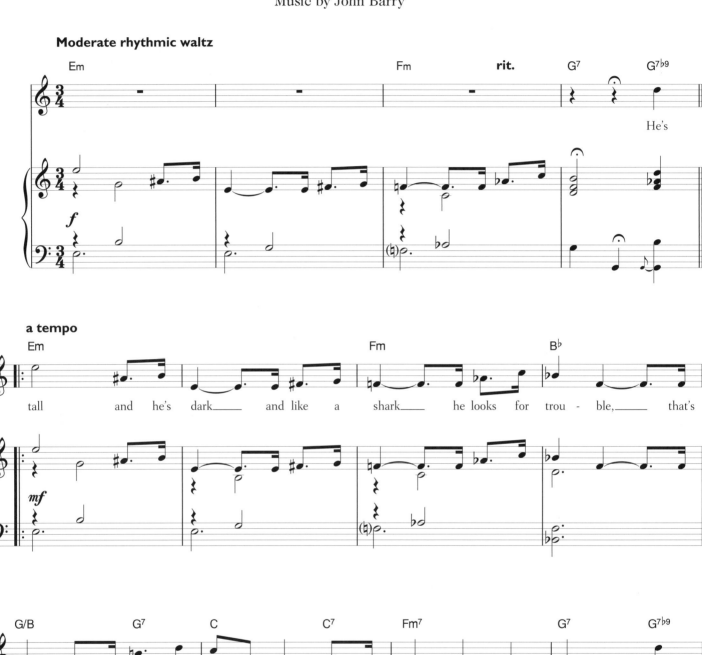

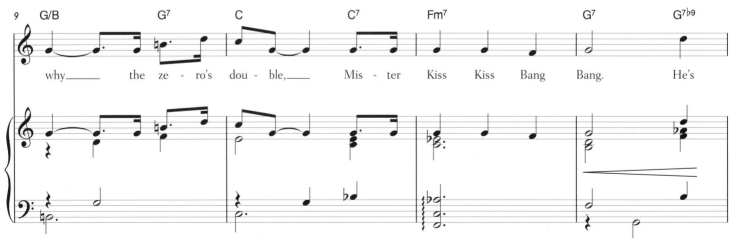

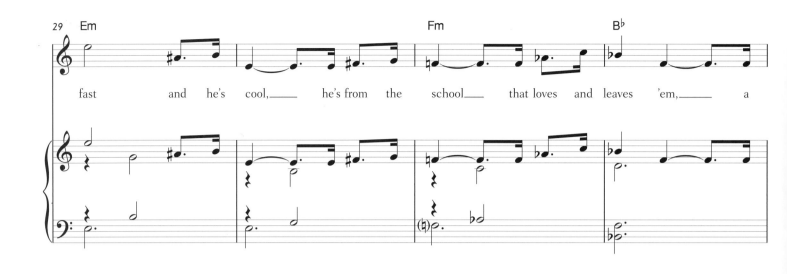

fast and he's cool,___ he's from the school___ that loves and leaves 'em,___ a

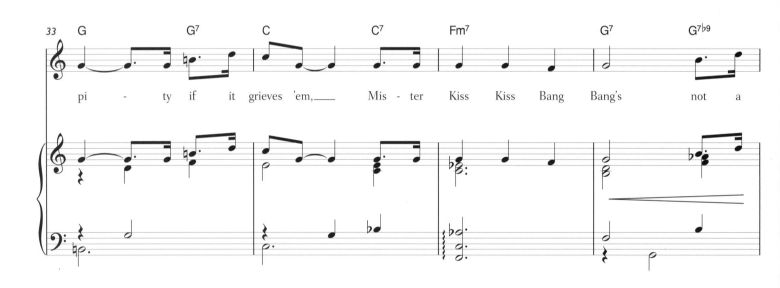

pi - ty if it grieves 'em,___ Mis - ter Kiss Kiss Bang Bang's not a

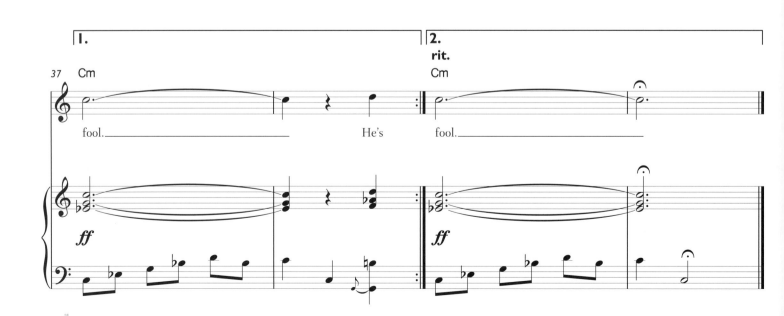

fool.___ He's fool.___

You Only Live Twice

(from 'You Only Live Twice')

Words by Leslie Bricusse
Music by John Barry

DIRECT FROM
LONDON'S WEST END

LESLIE BRICUSSE'S

DOCTOR
DOLITTLE

"SPELLBINDING ANIMAL MAGIC"
BRISTOL EVENING POST

SPECIAL GUEST STAR
PAUL NICHOLAS
IS THE DOCTOR ON
SATURDAYS

STARRING
PHILLIP
SCHOFIELD

Theatre Royal   Tuesday 3

Box

Theatre Street, Norwich,
Norfolk NR2 1RL

TOMMY
TUNE

DR
DOLITTLE

EVERYBODY'S MUSICAL

Book, Music and Lyrics

ORIGINAL MOTION PICTURE SOUNDTRACK
REX HARRISON
SAMANTHA   ANTHONY
EGGAR   as   NEWLEY

DOCTOR
DOLITTLE

music
and lyrics by
LESLIE
BRICUSSE
conducted by
LIONEL
NEWMAN

When I Look In Your Eyes

(from 'Doctor Dolittle')

Words and Music by Leslie Bricusse

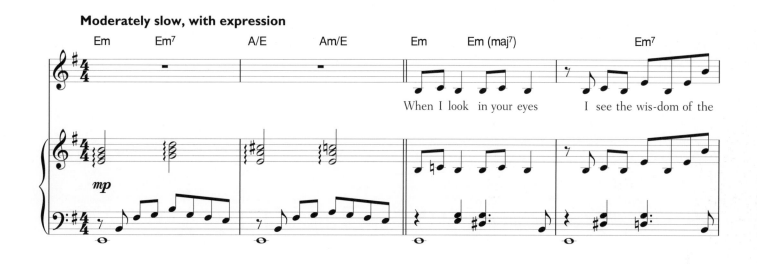

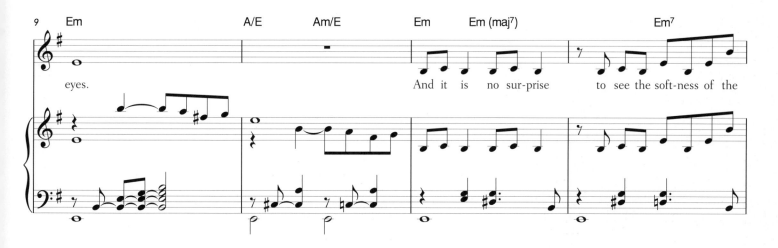

Talk To The Animals

(from 'Doctor Dolittle')

Words and Music by Leslie Bricusse

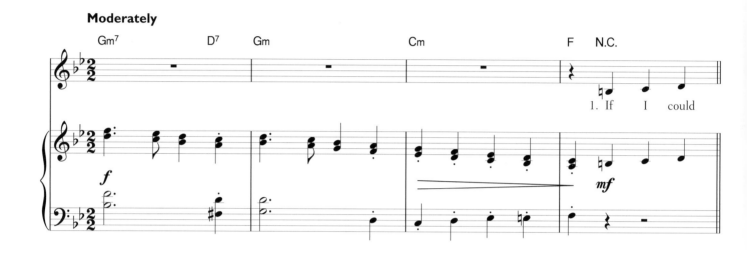

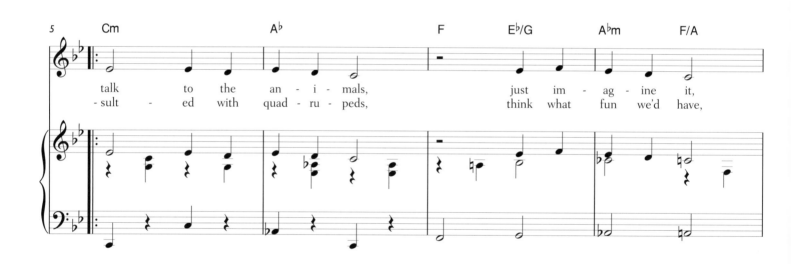

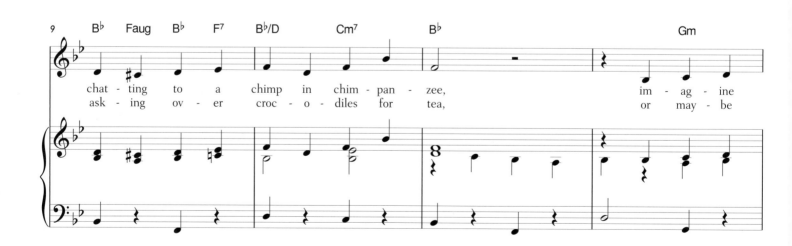

66

The Greatest

(from 'Sammy')

Words and Music by Leslie Bricusse

"SCROOGE"

Music and Lyrics by
LESLIE BRICUSSE

95c
in U.S.A.

S&S
STAGE AND SCREEN MUSIC. INC.
Executive offices:
9777 Wilshire Boulevard.
Beverly Hills, California 90212
Sales/shipping: 8th Floor -17 West 60th St.
New York, N.Y. 10023

Thank You Very Much

(from 'Scrooge')

Words and Music by Leslie Bricusse

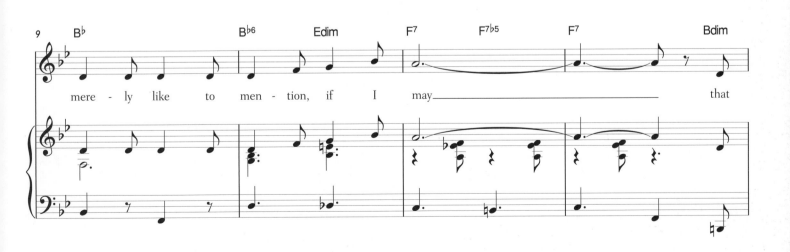

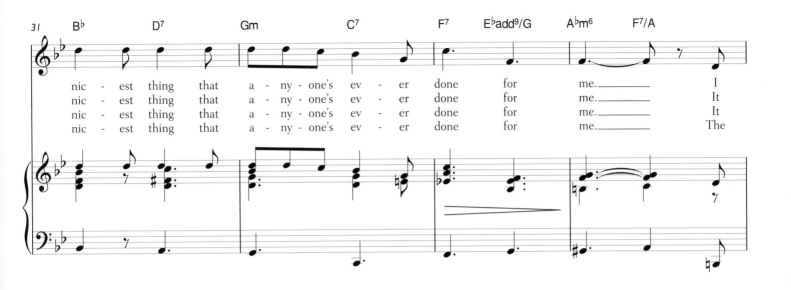

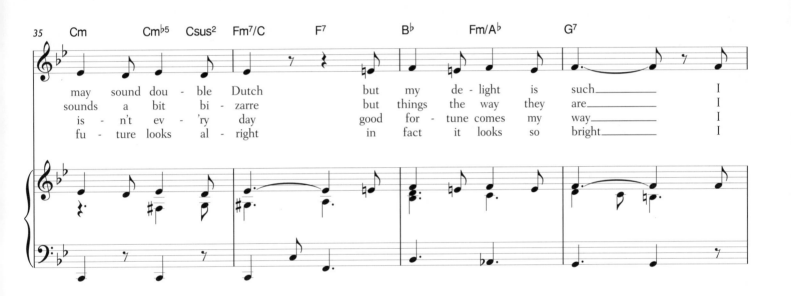

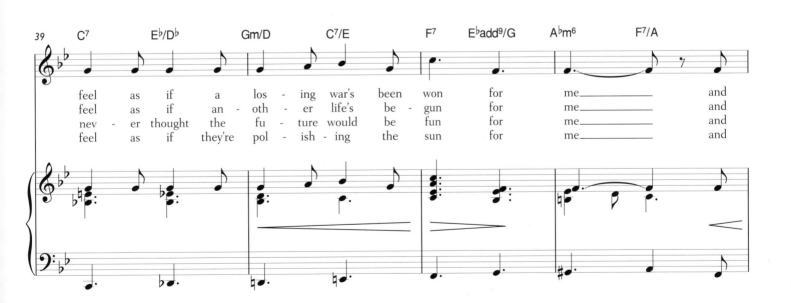

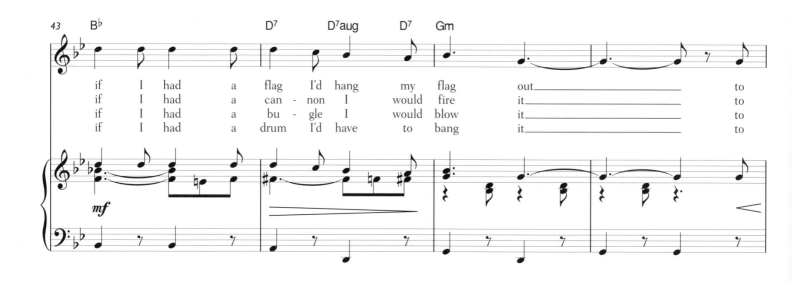

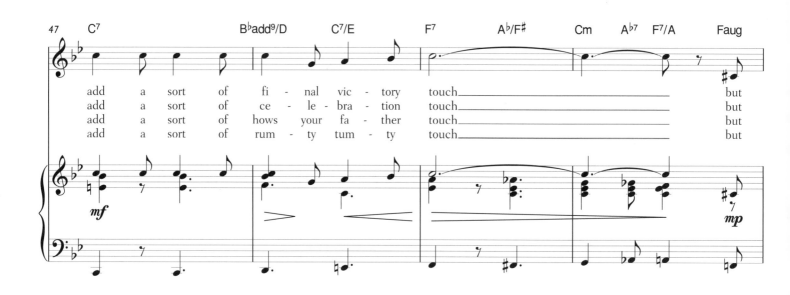

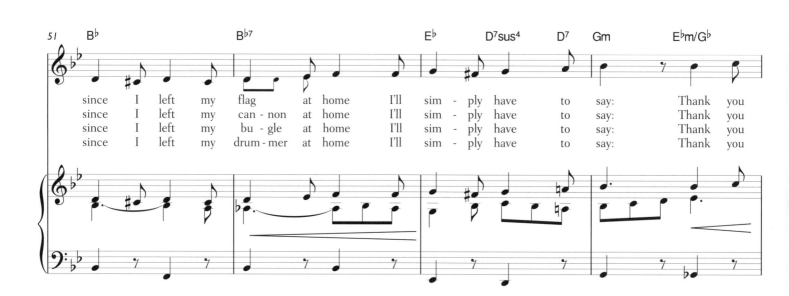

The Dream

(from the Motion Picture 'The Great Music Chase')

Words by Leslie Bricusse
Music by Pyotr Ilyich Tchaikovsky

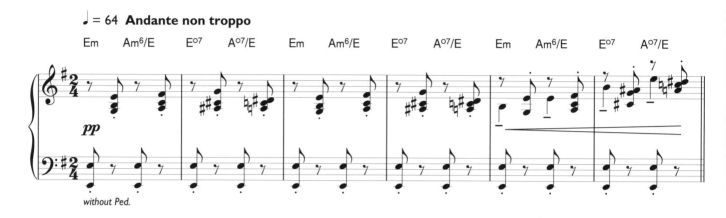

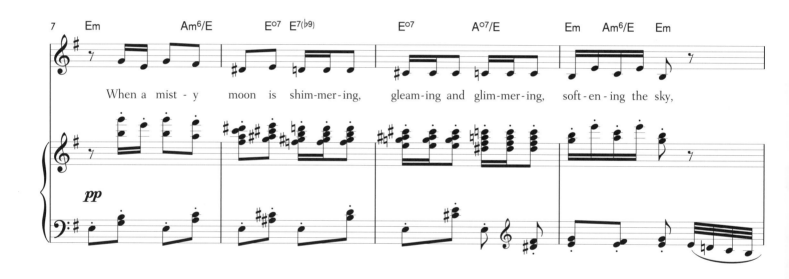

When a mist-y moon is shim-mer-ing, gleam-ing and glim-mer-ing, soft-en-ing the sky,

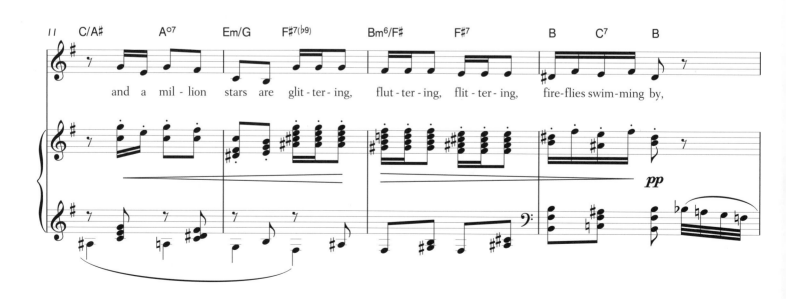

and a mil-lion stars are glit-ter-ing, flut-ter-ing, flit-ter-ing, fire-flies swim-ming by,

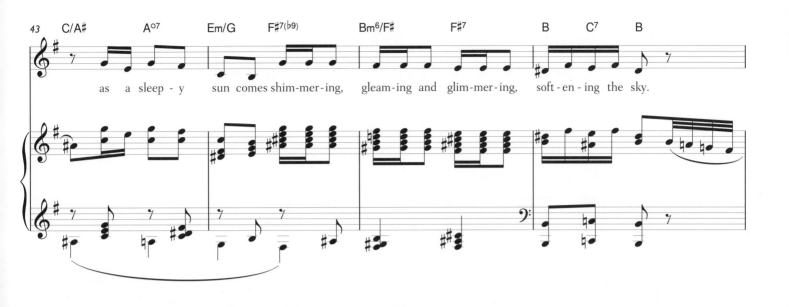

as a sleep-y sun comes shim-mer-ing, gleam-ing and glim-mer-ing, soft-en-ing the sky.

But I find my mind still wan-der-ing, won-der-ing, pon-der-ing: am I what I seem?

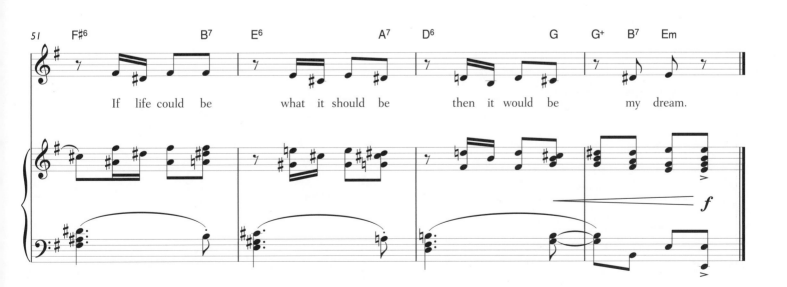

If life could be what it should be then it would be my dream.

Life!

(from the Motion Picture 'The Great Music Chase')

Words by Leslie Bricusse
Music by Pyotr Ilyich Tchaikovsky

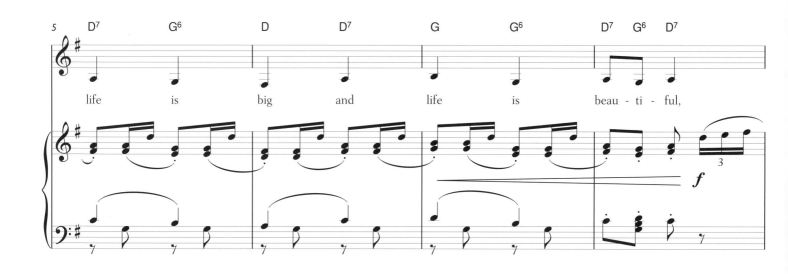

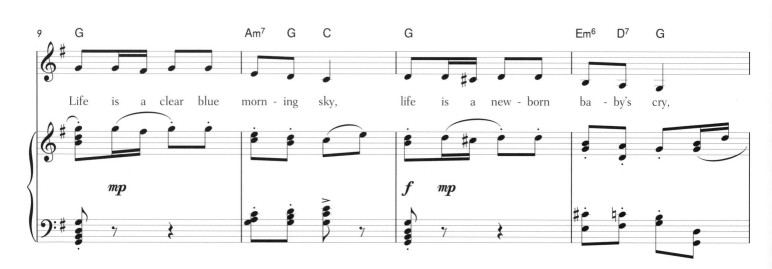

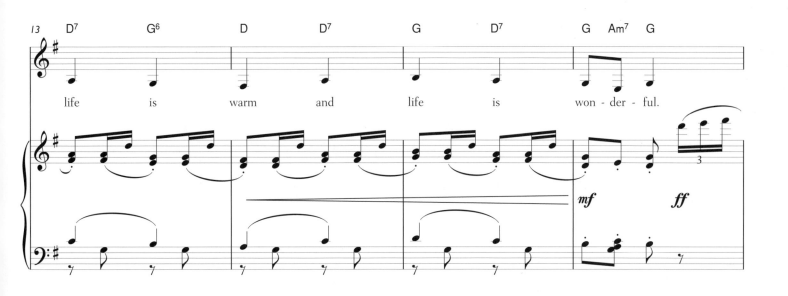

life is warm and life is won - der - ful.

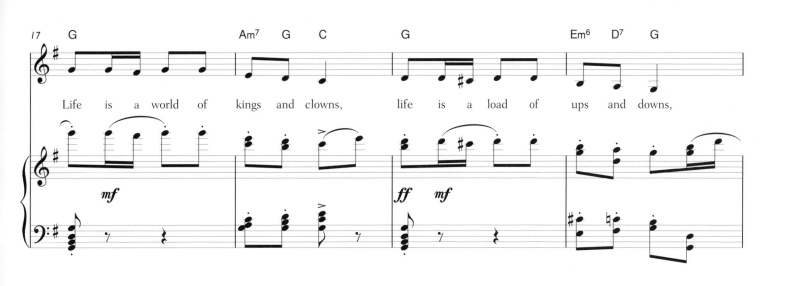

Life is a world of kings and clowns, life is a load of ups and downs,

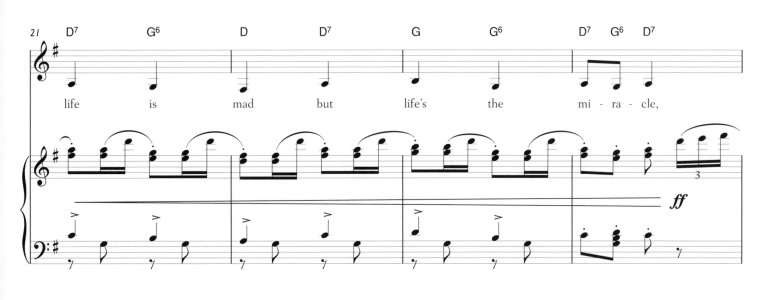

life is mad but life's the mi - ra - cle,

Life is a thou-sand jam-bo-rees, life is a box of mag-ic beans,

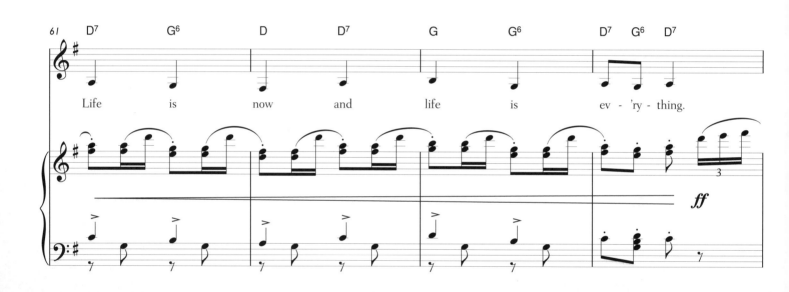

Life is now and life is ev-'ry-thing.

Life is-n't ev-'ry-day that's due, life is-n't ev-'ry-thing that you

Tell Me Who I Am

(from the Motion Picture 'The Great Music Chase')

Words by Leslie Bricusse
Music by Pyotr Ilyich Tchaikovsky

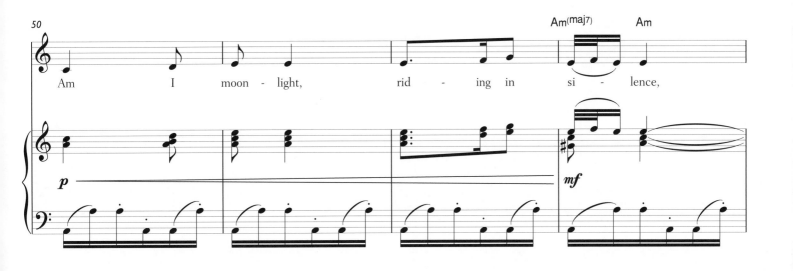

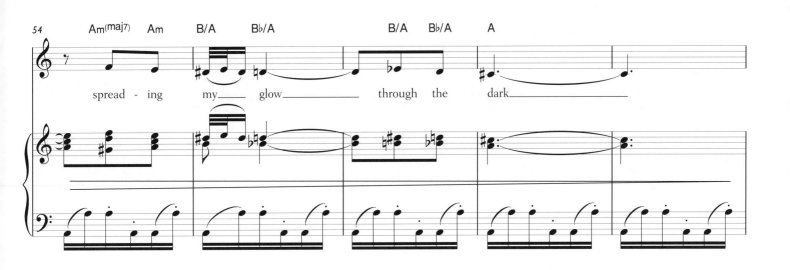

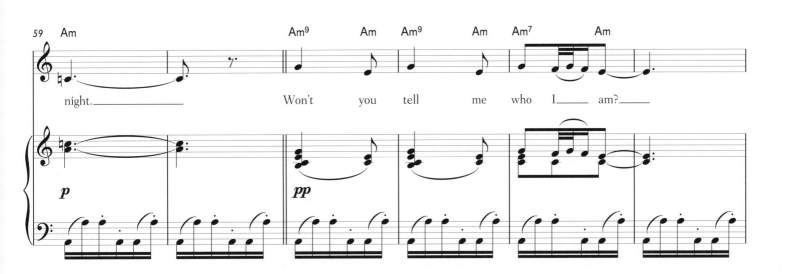

VOCAL SELECTIONS "WILLY WONKA & THE CHOCOLATE FACTORY"

Lyrics and Music by

LESLIE BRICUSSE and ANTHONY NEWLEY

Music Arranged and Conducted by WALTER SCHARF

DAVID L. WOLPER
presents

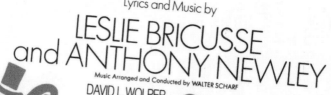

TARADAM MUSIC, Inc.
Executive offices:
9777 Wilshire Boulevard, Suite: 1015
Beverly Hills, California, 90212
Sales/shipping: 8th Floor—17 West 60th St.
New York, N.Y. 10023

Meet Charlie at the Chocolate Factory with his scrumdidilyumstious friends Willie Wonka, Mike Teevee, Augustus Gloop, Veruca Salt, Violet Beauregarde, Grandpa Joe, and a lot of delicious Oompa-Loompas.

Pure Imagination

(from 'Willy Wonka and the Chocolate Factory')

Words and Music by Leslie Bricusse and Anthony Newley

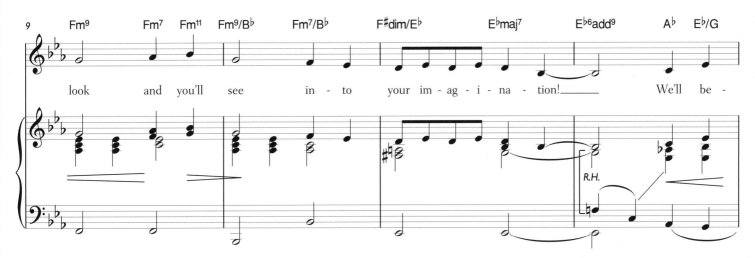

The Candy Man

(from 'Willy Wonka and the Chocolate Factory')

Words and Music by Leslie Bricusse and Anthony Newley

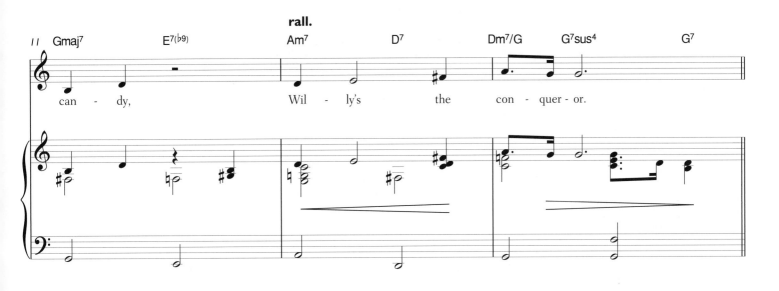

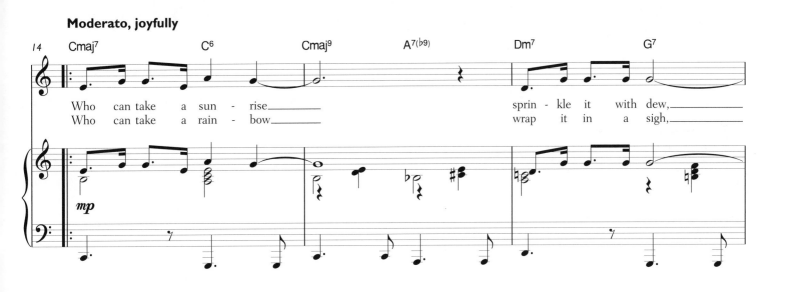

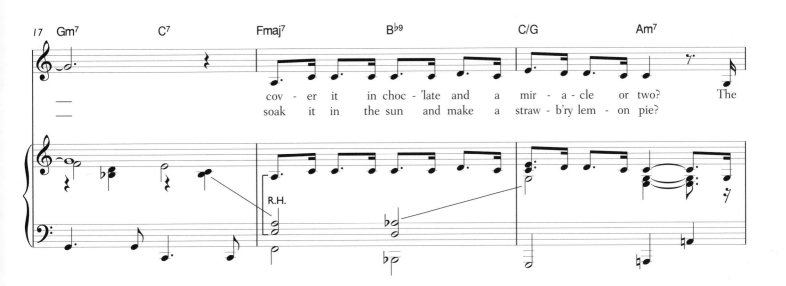

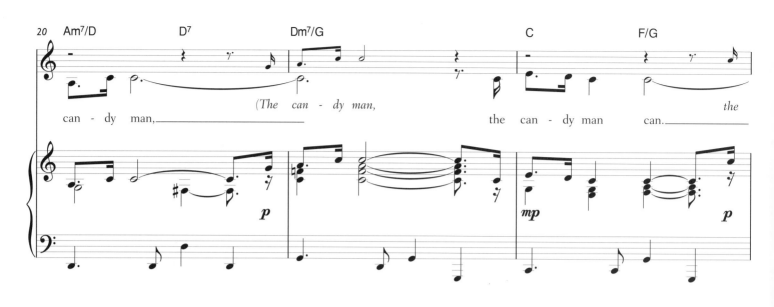

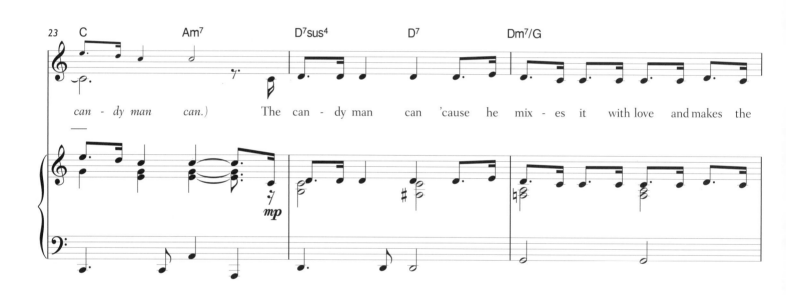

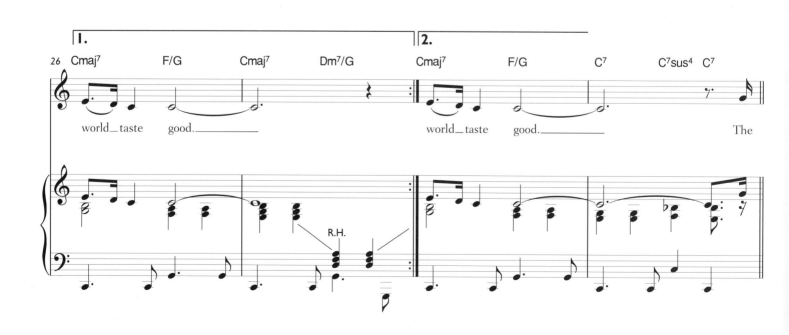

CAN YOU READ MY MIND?

Love Theme from "SUPERMAN"/A Warner Bros. Picture

LYRIC BY LESLIE BRICUSSE

MUSIC BY JOHN WILLIAMS

$ 1.50

WARNER BROS. PUBLICATIONS INC.
New York N.Y. 10019

Can You Read My Mind?

(Love Theme from 'Superman' a Warner Bros. Picture)

Words by Leslie Bricusse
Music by John Williams

JULIE ANDREWS

in A New Musical Comedy

VICTOR Victoria

MARQUIS THEATRE
BROADWAY & 46TH STREET

MAKEUP: CHRISSANNE DAVIS HAIR: MICHAELJOHN FRANCESCO SCAVULLO

ORIGINAL SOUNDTRACK
RECORDING

BLAKE EDWARDS'

VICTOR Victoria

GNPD 8038

WINNER 1982 Academy Award
Best Musical Score!

Music By
Henry Mancini

Lyrics By
Leslie Bricusse

GNP
Crescendo
RECORDS

Le Jazz Hot

(from 'Victor/Victoria')

Words by Leslie Bricusse
Music by Henry Mancini

112

London Is London

(from 'Sherlock Holmes - The Musical')

Words and Music by Leslie Bricusse

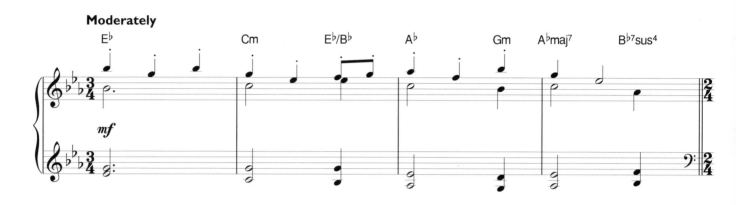

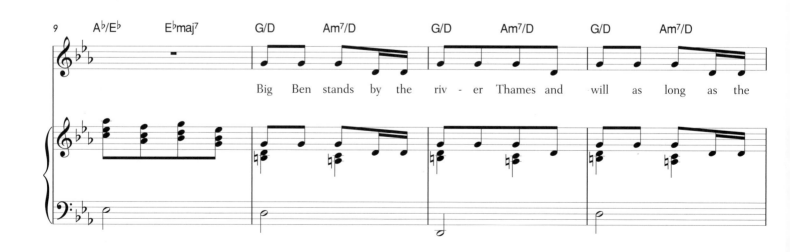

Somewhere In My Memory

(from the Motion Picture 'Home Alone')

Words by Leslie Bricusse
Music by John Williams

Gentle and with simplicity

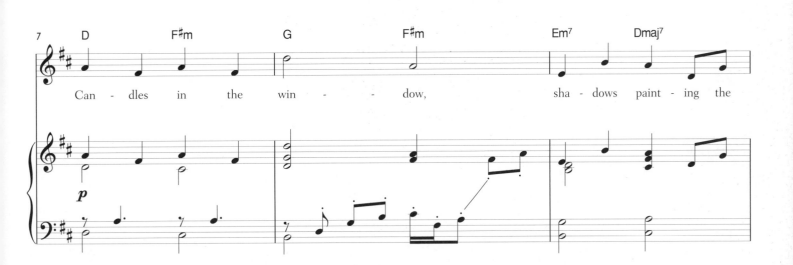

Can - dles in the win - - dow, sha - dows paint - ing the

Piano · Vocal · Guitar

This Is The Moment

from *Jekyll & Hyde*

The Musical

It's such a fine line between a good man and a bad.

Music by Frank Wildhorn
Lyrics by Leslie Bricusse

This Is The Moment

(from 'Jekyll & Hyde')

Words by Leslie Bricusse
Music by Leslie Bricusse and Frank Wildhorn

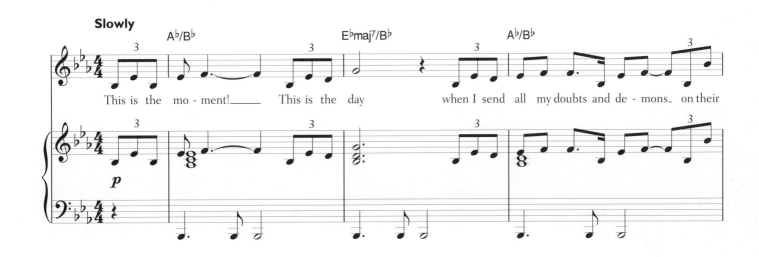

Paris In The Spring

(from 'A Few Words With George')

Words by Leslie Bricusse
Music by George Gershwin

Tempo blues
Andante ma con ritmo deciso

Here I am in Pa - ris... (Sweet young lamb in Pa - ris...)

No - - - - - where's quite like Pa - ris in the Spring!_____

So_____ I go to Pa - ris in the

134

poco meno

Pa - ris is a love song, the "can't have to much of" song lov - ers bring.___

poco accel.   a tempo

cresc.

And oh___

poco rit.

___ when that old moon be - gins to glow,   you will see a world like none you

a tempo con moto

know!   No -   where's quite like Pa - ris in the Spring!___

Music

(from 'A Few Words With George')

Words by Leslie Bricusse
Music by George Gershwin

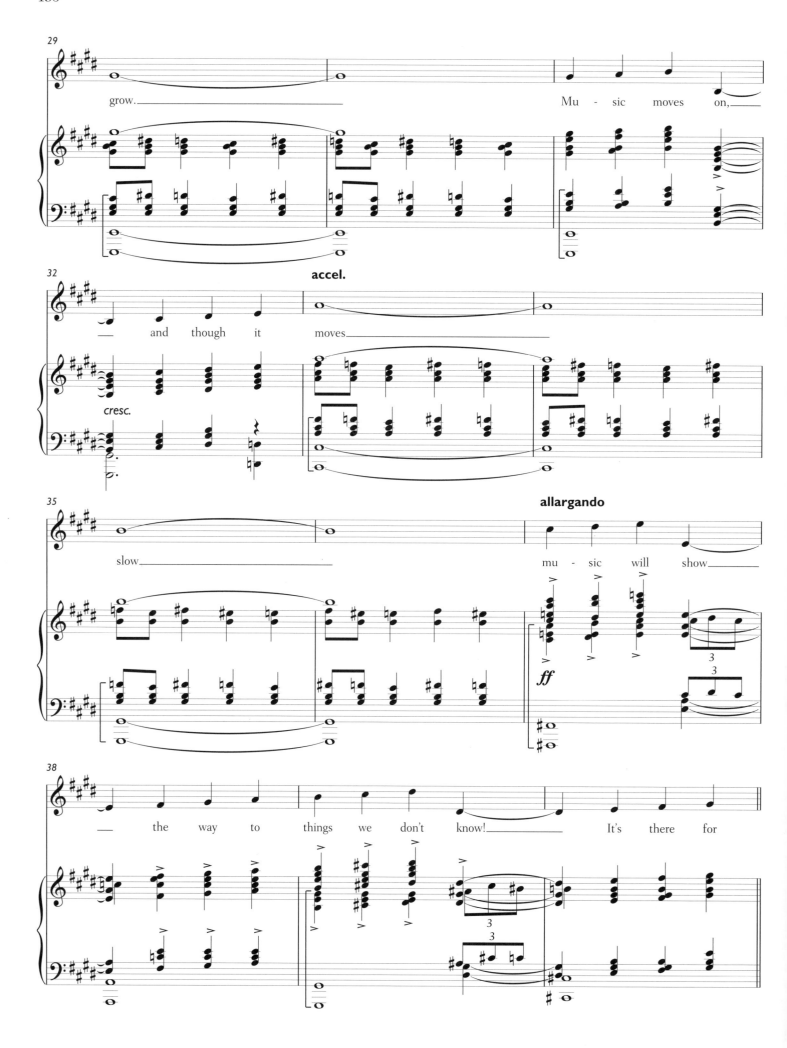

A New Kind Of Music

(from 'A Few Words With George')

Words by Leslie Bricusse
Music by George Gershwin

Ev-'ry-one lis-tened an' smiled as the mu - sic filled the air

hap-py 'n' free as a child in a world with - out__ a care, peo-ple com-plete-ly be-guiled all a-round me ev - 'ry-where!

I felt the mood in ev - 'ry - one there! At last we had a friend we could share!

It's got a rhy-thm,

a spe-cial rhy-thm this plan-et ain't heard be-fore!__ An' that's the rhy-thm we call

Jazz! Full of piz-zazz and such raz-za-ma-tazz__ that it knocks__ ya down flat__ on the floor!

The World That I See

(from 'A Few Words With George')

Words by Leslie Bricusse
Music by George Gershwin

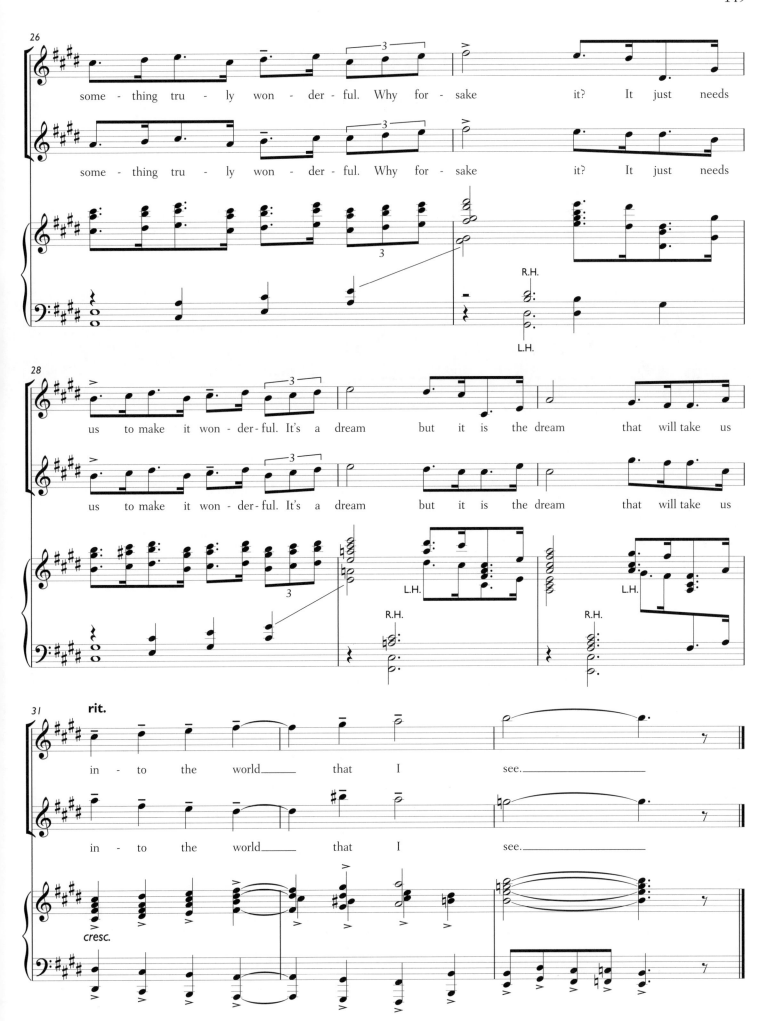

What About Me?

(from 'Sunday Dallas')

Words and Music by Leslie Bricusse

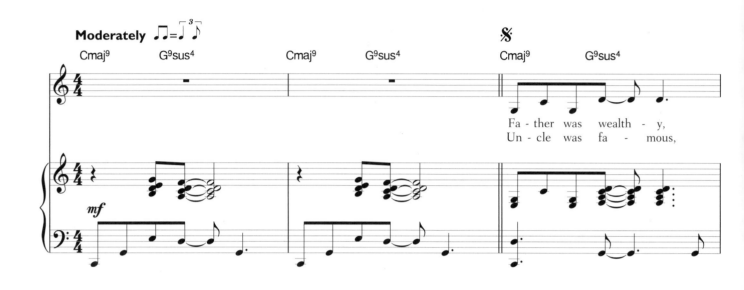

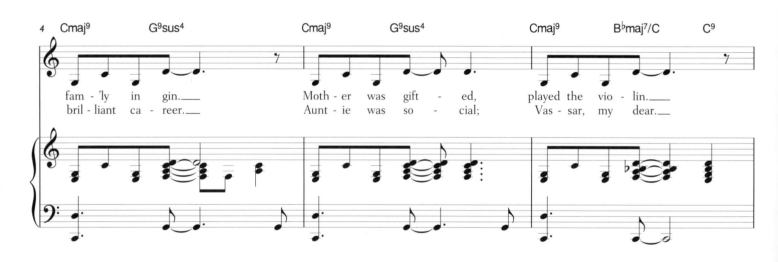

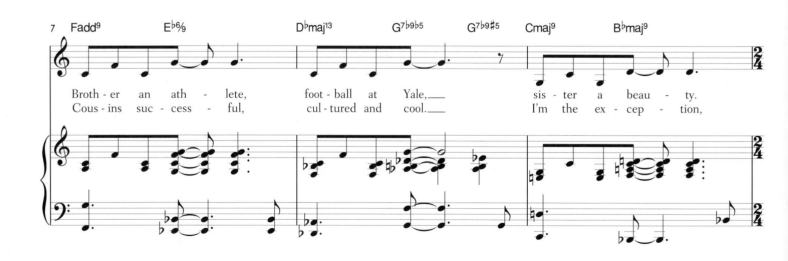

Tomorrow With Me

(from 'Noah's Ark')

Words and Music by Leslie Bricusse

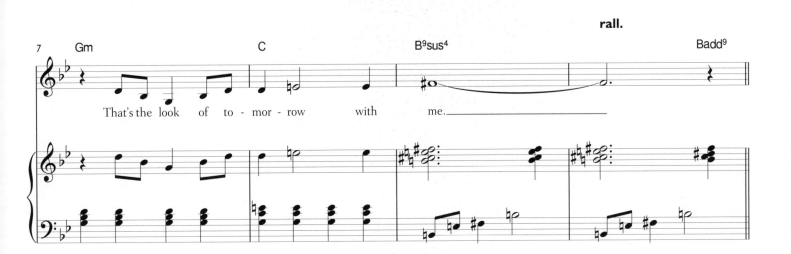

Think Positive

(from the Stage Show Roald Dahl's 'Willy Wonka')

Words and Music by Leslie Bricusse

The Only Man For Me

(from 'Sammy')

Words and Music by Leslie Bricusse

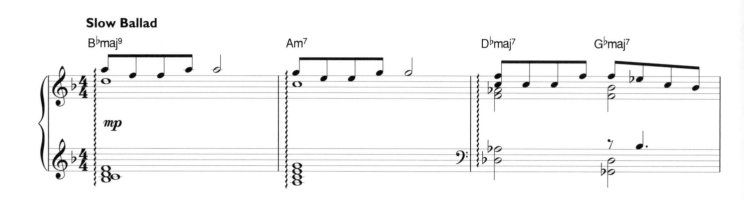

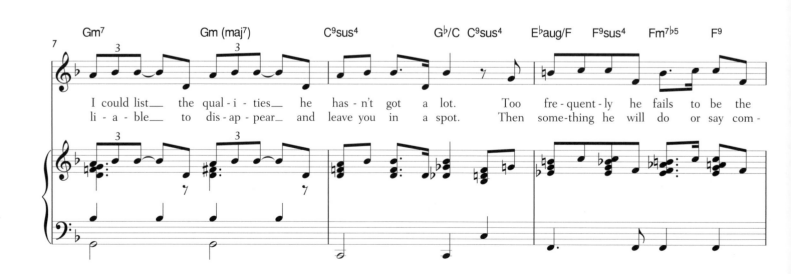

164

The Perfect Song

Words by Leslie Bricusse
Music by Andrew Lloyd Webber

with pedal

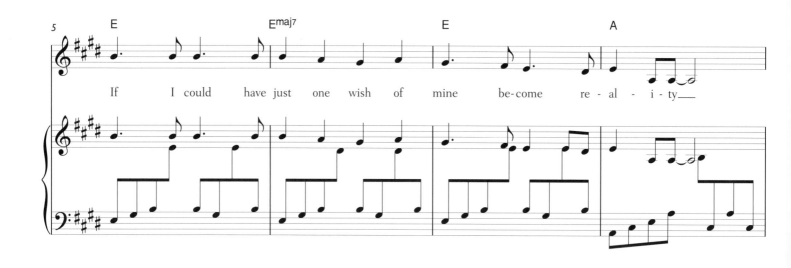

If I could have just one wish of mine be-come re-al-i-ty____

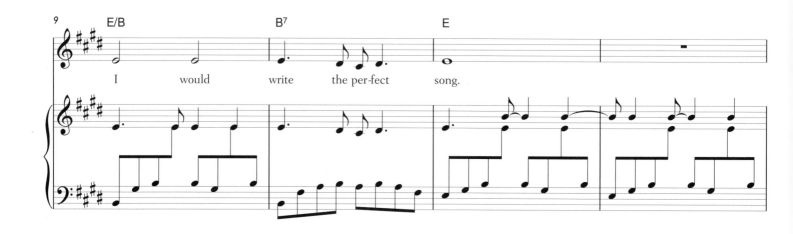

I would write the per-fect song.

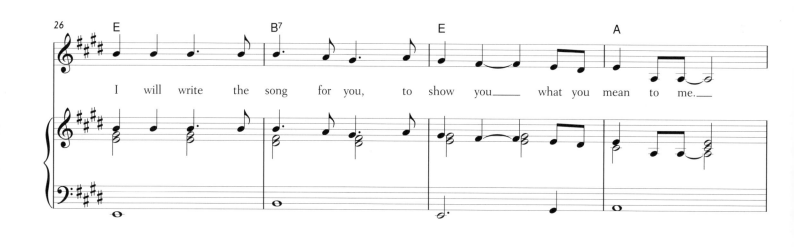

I will write the song for you, to show you__ what you mean to me.__

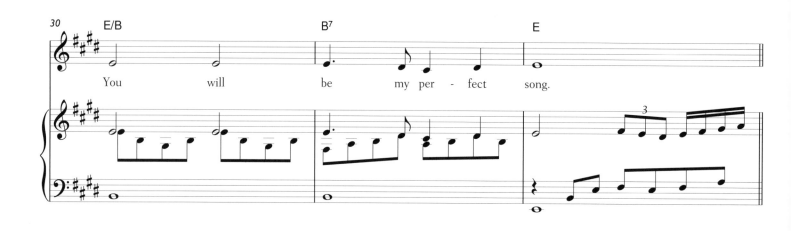

You will be my per - fect song.

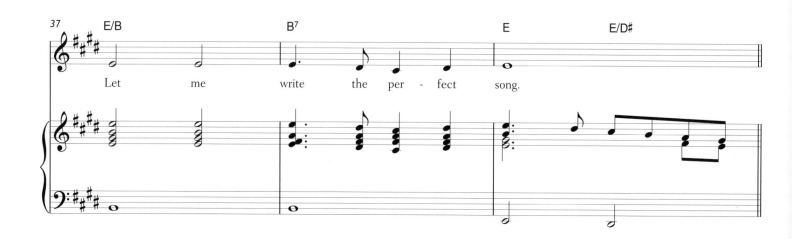

Let me write the per - fect song.

You Are All The Music

(from 'Sunday Dallas')

Words and Music by Leslie Bricusse

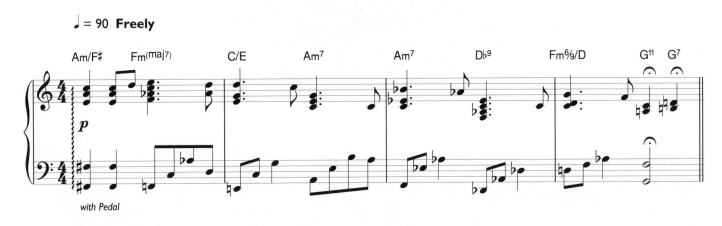

You are all the mus - ic, you are all the love - ly things that

make my life worth liv - ing,_____ You are all the prec - ious gifts fate

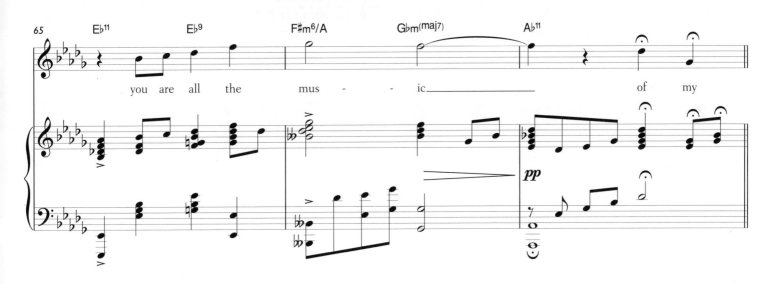

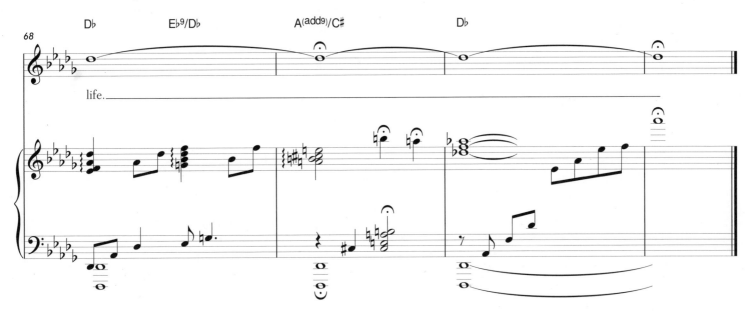

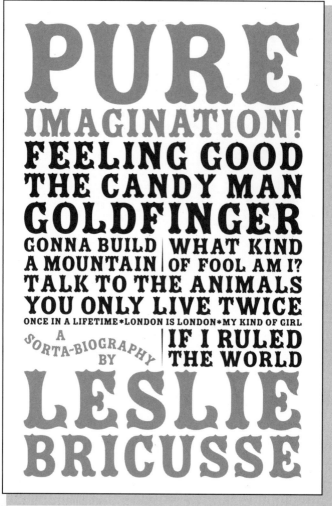

PURE
IMAGINATION!
FEELING GOOD
THE CANDY MAN
GOLDFINGER
GONNA BUILD | WHAT KIND
A MOUNTAIN | OF FOOL AM I?
TALK TO THE ANIMALS
YOU ONLY LIVE TWICE
ONCE IN A LIFETIME * LONDON IS LONDON * MY KIND OF GIRL
A
SORTA-BIOGRAPHY | IF I RULED
BY | THE WORLD
LESLIE
BRICUSSE

ISBN: 0-571-53930-0

PURE IMAGINATION!
A sorta-biography by Leslie Bricusse
The life & good times of one of the world's favourite songwriters

Leslie's story of talent, determination and a little bit of luck will take you on a fascinating journey from humble beginnings through this hardest of businesses to dizzying heights. He built his name and reputation first in the West End of London, then on Broadway and finally Hollywood.

Over the past sixty years, Leslie has collaborated with a dazzling array of stars and sensational writing partnerships, all of whom remain close and long-lasting friends. This is a hugely entertaining and fascinating insight into the life of one of the most celebrated and successful writers for stage and screen.

"His catalogue of songs is enormous – his achievements endless. Anyone who has written What Kind Of Fool Am I? and My Old Man's A Dustman should be revered forever."

Elton John

To buy Faber Music publications or to find out about the full range of titles available please contact your local music retailer or Faber Music sales enquiries:

Faber Music Ltd, Burnt Mill, Elizabeth Way, Harlow CM20 2HX
Tel: +44 (0) 1279 82 89 82   Fax: +44 (0) 1279 82 89 83
sales@fabermusic.com   fabermusicstore.com